FONDUE
and FURS

Oliver Preston

FONDUE
and FURS

Oliver Preston.

BEVERSTON PRESS

For Vivien, Amber and Rex

First published in Great Britain in 2011 by

BEVERSTON PRESS

Tetbury, Glos GL8 8TT

British Library cataloguing in Publication Data
A catalogue record for this title is available from The British Library

ISBN 978 0 9549936 4 1

Designed by boinggraphics.co.uk
Printed by Gutenberg Press, Malta

Gstaad
'The arrival of the international jet set.'

INTRODUCTION

The road that winds its way up to Gstaad from the castle of Gruyères is lined with seventeenth century villages and chalets that are festooned with flowers in summer. The Simmental cattle punctuate the pastures, and conifers bravely forest the steep slopes on either side of the valley. In winter it is a wonderland. You know you have arrived at Gstaad when you catch your first glimpse of the fairy tale Palace Hotel, its neogothic turrets lit up against the night sky. Come and play, they say.

The village is in the Canton of Berne and famous as one of the most exclusive ski resorts in the world, the winter campus of the Institut Le Rosey and home to the John F Kennedy School, and to many famous part-time residents and celebrity visitors. It effortlessly combines a chic mountain ambience with a local rural economy, and is home to 220 kilometres of ski pistes at up to 3000 metres above sea level.

The high street is a showcase for haut couture boutiques - Cartier, Ralph Lauren, Hermès, and Chopard, amongst others - and it juxtaposes ridiculous ostentation, with the everyday lives of the locals and farmers. A chauffeur driven limo draws up inconveniently in the centre of the village and disgorges the fur coats (and their body guards), these citizens of the world who are intent on a little, but rather extravagant, shopping. The next day a farmer will nonchalantly drive his prize Simmental cattle through the mêlée, going about his business. Everyone has dogs. Large dogs, little dogs, hand held, smooth, hairy; they are as international as their gilded owners. Après ski is a cacophony of beautiful people and locals in restaurants, enjoying the Saanerland delicacies of bündnerfleisch and of fondues and raclettes. The Gstaadois ski hard during the day and play hard every night, it is a cocktail of fondues and furs, of exclusive clubs, and chalet hopping, and it all ends up in the lobby bar or dancing at the Palace until late, to see and be seen, before slipping away to bed. Or someone else's.

I first went to Gstaad in the 1960s, staying at our family chalet on the Wispile and larked about on the nursery slopes with my swiss cousins. A season spent working as a waiter on the Wasserngrat presaged a love for the village, and Vivien and I were married there in 2002. Like all Gstaad habitués there is a strong desire to pass on to our own children the magic of this mountain oasis, but an innate desire not to tell anyone else about its secret formula. I love observing the people, its institutions, and of course hitting the slopes. Other resorts may boast more snow, longer runs, and more majestic moguls. They have skiing with a bit of lunch. Gstaad is lunch with a bit of skiing, amongst the trees, and wonderful off piste, touring, and mountain restaurants that you just don't want to leave.

Gstaad is a special place, but it's probably not for you. You really should try Méribel, or Verbier, St. Moritz or Aspen. You'll have a much better time. Leave Gstaad to us - to me, my family, and my friends. I'm just not sure that I can trust you to keep a secret.

OLIVER PRESTON.

'Who does your snow?'

'I hear he's going to turn it into a hotel.'

'They have a very small kingdom,
somewhere between the Eggli and the Wasserngrat.'

'Love at first sight.'

Gstaad
'Celebrating the arrival of the first flake of snow.'

'Now, it's YOUR turn.'

'Do I look as though I need a work permit?'

'Oh my God,
she's missed a gate.
She'll have to
go back to the
beginning...'

'Very nice, darling. Did you keep the receipt?'

'What an amazing coincidence. I'm looking at your file as we speak.'

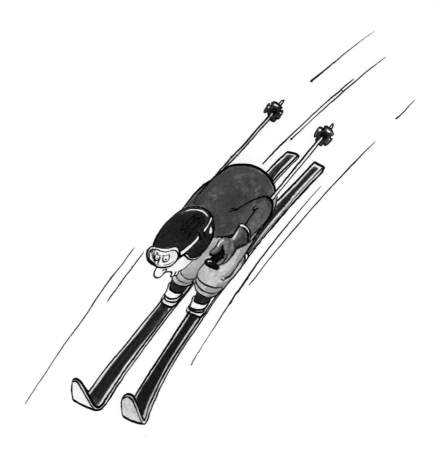

'I'm sure daddy would have beaten you if he'd really tried.'

'Do I look as though I'm overweight??!'

'No, let me. You did lunch.'

'The Eagle Club Ski Team goes to the races.'

'Skied here all my life', you said. 'Know these pistes like the back of my hand', you said. 'Follow me...', you said!

'Ah yes, that's my husband.
I recognise my shopping.'

'Would you like to know what else I learnt at Finishing School?'

'Oh dear, my ski pass doesn't work. I'll have to go shopping instead.'

'The Visitor'

The Gstaad Ski School for Shopaholics

'If I sleep with you tonight, it doesn't mean I'll ski with you in the morning.'

'Don't just stand there. Call a designer.'

' I'm afraid it's Gstaaditis but it's most unusual to see it with skis.'

'Was it really such a good idea to tell him
that you were a downhill champion?'

'A packet of Benson and Hedges,
and my friend here will have a large Cohiba.'

'Let's go somewhere else. There's absolutely nobody here.'

'This year we've taken a chalet by the Palace.'

'Sometimes I think you love Gstaad more than me.'

'Darling, it is traditional
to ski down after lunch.'

'Listen, we'll pay you 10,000 Francs
if you DON'T stop the train in Gstaad.'

'The Gstaad Yacht Club
goes to the races.'

'Book me a table for lunch with my third wife.
Somewhere I won't bump into my first or second wife.'

'I'm going to lead an independent life
as soon as you've packed my bags.'

'You'll love the skiing in Gstaad.
There are never any queues at the lifts.'

'You don't think I invited you to Gstaad for the skiing?'

OLIVER PRESTON.

Après Ski Gstaad

'Well it certainly buggers-up our restaurant booking at one o'clock.'

'The KNEES, Mrs.Pickering. Bend zee knees.'

'Hi, I'm on the cable car.'

'Caught Short'

'Gucci, Gucci, Choos...'

'Can you do your impression of a fish, because daddy says you drink like one.'

"Then I said to her, 'If only you spent as much on the ski lessons as you did on the ski outfits.' "

'It was either my husband or my shopping.'

OLIVER PRESTON.

'I see it's very cold out on the slopes today.'

'You look a million dollars. Is that how much it cost?'

'Of course coming to the Alps with Hannibal,
makes us very, very old Gstaad.'

'...and did you pack the bags yourself?'

'She doesn't turn RIGHT on planes.'

'It's the man to repair the cuckoo clock.'

'I've taken a large position in gold, because gold never goes down.'

'HENRY! You're skating on VERY thin ice.'

'Remember dad, she's mine, not yours.'

'I could get a job, but it would ruin my hair.'

'Anything WITHOUT cheese?'

'Gosh, we're hot!'

'It'll have to wait until I've cleared up this DREADFUL mess.'

OLIVER PRESTON.

'Night Skiing'

'He skied for Switzerland until he took up playing the saw.'

'You've got a fine pair of skis.'

'Snap'

'It was either him, or us.'

'Cut the crap and show us your willy.'

'More windswept dear –
it needs to look as though I've had a really hard day's skiing.'

'Eton, Cambridge,
The Guards.'

'JFK, Le Rosey,
The Palace Hotel.'

'Darling, it's so nice to be celebrating your 39th birthday yet again.'

'Well, something's eating into our profits...'

ACKNOWLEDGEMENTS

Illustration Acknowledgements
First published
6, 43, 51 *Gstaad My Love Magazine 2008-2010*
15, 18, 19, 22, 36, 52, 56, 58, 68, 70, 73, 74, 87, 94 *The Field Magazine*
5, 66, *The Polo Magazine*.

By the same author

Liquid Limericks (2001)	Robson Books	with Alistair Sampson
Larder Limericks (2004)	Robson Books	with Alistair Sampson
Shall we join the Men (2005)	Beverston Press	
Modern Cautionary Verses (2006)	Constable Robinson	with Charlie Ottley
Hitting the Slopes (2008)	Beverston Press	
How to be Asked Again (2009)	Quiller	with Rosie Nickerson
Out of Town (2010)	Beverston Press	
Out for a Duck (2010)	Quiller	with Ian Valentine
Another Log on the Fire (2011)	Beverston Press	
Real Men Drink Port (2011)	Quiller	with Ben Howkins

My thanks to Simon Russell at Boing for the design and layout preparation, and Bobby Blackstock at The Gutenberg Press, Malta, for printing and advice and to Jill Schumm at Beverston Press Ltd. Thank you to Andrea and Laura Scherz and the staff of the Gstaad Palace, Hans-Ueli Tschanz, Frank Müller, and Michelle Bagnall and everyone at Papeterie Cadonau.

Prints and greeting cards available from '*Fondue and Furs*'
Visit www.beverstonpress.com or call +44 (0) 1666 502638